THE BADASS METALLICA TRIVIA BOOK

Uncover The Epic History Behind
The American Heavy Metal Band!

By

Dale Raynes

ISBN: 978-1-955149-02-0

bp@purplelink.org

Please consider writing a review!

Just visit: purplelink.org/review

TABLE OF CONTENTS

INTRODUCTION

One of the most influential heavy metal bands of all time, Metallica, is a band known around the world. Their fast, aggressive sound and deep, unapologetic lyrics initially stole the headbanging affection of the underground metal scene. Metallica continued to evolve their music across several metal subgenres, building their fanbase worldwide, until they exploded into fame.

From the start, Metallica aimed for world domination, and they certainly achieved their goal. Actively releasing music and touring for nearly 40 years at venues around the world, they brought American heavy metal to all that would listen. Anyone who considers themselves a rock or metal music fan is at least familiar with the legacy of Metallica. To help you strengthen your connection with their origins, music, and lives— interesting facts, stories, and historical moments are featured in this book, *The Badass Metallica Trivia Book.*

This trivia book covers the history and influence of Metallica beginning with their formation until their status in the year 2021. A series of multiple choice and true or false questions open each chapter, with corresponding answers on the page following.

Additional interesting facts and stories close each chapter in the "Did You Know" portion, so you can depart this book with an in-depth knowledge of, and connection to, the band.

The information and statistics in this book are up to date as of early 2021. Because the band is still active and intends to continue making music and touring, more stories may unfold after the release of this book. Records and stats may fluctuate in the coming years with future releases, tours, and potential awards, but their background history will remain consistent.

Use this book to test your knowledge with a round of trivia about Metallica's history, people, stories, moments, and music. Whether you consider yourself a Metallica fanatic or are seeking to discover more about the band, this book offers the opportunity to reinforce your knowledge of one of the most prolific and successful metal bands in history.

Let's see how much you know about Metallica!

CHAPTER 1:

HISTORY AND ORIGINS

TRIVIA TIME!

1. What year was Metallica formed?

   a. 1980
   b. 1981
   c. 1982
   d. 1983

2. Metallica started as an answer to an advertisement in what Los Angeles newspaper?

   a. *L.A. Times*
   b. *Los Angeles Sentinel*
   c. *The Recycler*
   d. *Larchmont Chronicle*

3. True or False: Metallica drummer Lars Ulrich moved to Los Angeles at age sixteen to train as a professional tennis player, like his father.

4. Metallica's first widely circulated demo was titled what?

   a. *No Life 'til Leather*
   b. *No Love 'til Fire*

    c. *No Metal 'til Death*
    d. *No Peace in Hell*

5. Although Metallica was founded in Los Angeles, what California city were they based in for most of their career?

    a. Sacramento
    b. San Francisco
    c. San Diego
    d. Long Beach

6. True or False: James Hetfield's first impression of Lars Ulrich's drumming was that he was not a good drummer.

7. Metallica was considered pioneers of which subgenre of metal music?

    a. Black metal
    b. Thrash metal
    c. Death metal
    d. Hair metal

8. The "Big Four" heavy metal bands of the world include Metallica, Megadeth, Anthrax, and which of the following?

    a. Iron Maiden
    b. Black Sabbath
    c. Slayer
    d. Motorhead

9. True or False: When Metallica started as a band, the members were all aged twenty and under.

10. Where did Metallica play their first live performance?

    a. The Fillmore, San Francisco
    b. Casbah, San Diego
    c. Fox Theater, Oakland
    d. Radio City, Anaheim

11. In what year did Metallica first start touring?

    a. 1980
    b. 1981
    c. 1983
    d. 1985

12. True or False: Lars Ulrich designed the classic Metallica logo used on many of the band's releases.

13. In what city was the studio where Metallica recorded their debut album?

    a. Rochester, New York
    b. Albany, New York
    c. Los Angeles, California
    d. San Francisco, California

14. Located in El Cerrito, California, what was the name of the now-infamous location where Metallica lived in 1983?

    a. Mansion Metallica
    b. Man-tallica
    c. Metalli-Mansion
    d. 'Tallica Mansion

15. True or False: Metallica immediately hit the mainstream music scene when they debuted their first album.

16. Before officially forming the band together, James Hetfield was recruited to sing and play rhythm guitar with Lars Ulrich for a compilation album of what name?

    a. Shred Metal
    b. Metal Mania
    c. Mega Metal
    d. Metal Massacre

17. Outside of the U.S., in what country has Metallica played the most, at over one hundred concerts?

    a. Britain
    b. Germany
    c. Denmark
    d. Canada

18. True or False: As Metallica started gaining fame in the 1980s, they embraced the glam metal image and wore flashy stage clothes.

19. As a child, what was the first instrument James Hetfield played and took lessons for?

    a. Piano
    b. Guitar
    c. Drums
    d. Violin

ANSWERS

1. B - 1981

2. C - *The Recycler*

3. True

4. A - *No Life 'til Leather*

5. B - San Francisco

6. True - He also thought Lars smelled funny.

7. B - Thrash metal

8. C - Slayer

9. True

10. D - Radio City, Anaheim

11. C - 1982

12. False - James Hetfield designed the logo for Metallica.

13. A - Rochester, New York

14. C - Metalli-Mansion

15. False - Metallica started in the metal underground.

16. D - Metal Massacre

17. B – Germany but Canada is a close third

18. False - Metallica remains anti-glam metal.

19. A - Piano

DID YOU KNOW?

- Metallica's name came from Lars Ulrich's friend, Ron Quintana, who was brainstorming names for a fanzine. He was torn between MetalMania or Metallica, and after hearing the two names, Ulrich wanted Metallica for his band name. This is basically lifted verbatim from Wikipedia: "The band name came from Ulrich's friend Ron Quintana, who was brainstorming names for a fanzine and was considering MetalMania or Metallica. After hearing the two names, Ulrich wanted Metallica for his band, so he suggested Quintana use MetalMania instead."

- Early in their career, Hetfield referred to Metallica's sound as power metal and later would be classified as thrash metal. The term "thrash metal" was coined in 1984 in reference to Anthrax's song, "Metal Thrashing Mad."

- British heavy bands such as Diamond Head, Iron Maiden, and Motorhead were some of the first inspirations for members of Metallica, especially Lars Ulrich. The movement at the time was called new wave British heavy metal.

- Metallica's first appearance on a record was not their own album but on a compilation album by Metal Blade Records called *Metal Massacre*, where the band's name was misspelled as "Mettallica."

- Now one of the biggest-selling metal acts in history, Metallica initially struggled to find an established record label and get signed. At the time, their aggressive music was not considered commercial. Therefore, only independent labels were interested in them at first.

- The Bay Area culture of San Francisco was in inspiration for early Metallica. Early thrash metal thrived in this area. Aside from Metallica, the area spawned innovative, pioneering bands such as Testament, Exodus, Death Angel, and Possessed.

CHAPTER 2:

KEY PEOPLE

TRIVIA TIME!

1. Who produced Metallica's first album?
   a. Bob Rock
   b. Paul Curcio
   c. Kirk Hammett
   d. Fleming Rasmussen

2. True or False: James Hetfield identifies Aerosmith as being a main musical influence in his childhood and inspiring him to play guitar.

3. After recording the Metallica album *Kill 'Em All,* who did Kirk Hammett take guitar lessons from?
   a. Van Halen
   b. Eric Clapton
   c. Joe Satriani
   d. Slash

4. True or False: Robert Trujillo was offered one million dollars upfront to join Metallica as their bass player.

5. When Lars Ulrich was nine years old, his father took him to see what band that would ignite his passion for music and inspire him to start his own band?

   a. Deep Purple
   b. Diamond Head
   c. Guns 'n Roses
   d. Anthrax

6. What producer would help bring Metallica mainstream commercial success with their eponymous album *Metallica*?

   a. Jon Zazula
   b. Bob Rock
   c. Fleming Rasmussen
   d. Rick Rubin

7. As Metallica gained traction, who is considered to be their first official manager, signing them to his own record label for the first time?

   a. Paul Circio
   b. Fleming Rasmussen
   c. Jon Zazula
   d. Bob Rock

8. With his management company, Q Prime, who managed Metallica along with several other metal bands including AC/DC, Scorpions, and Def Leppard?

   a. Peter Mensch
   b. Doc McGhee

    c. Warren Entner

    d. Rick Sales

9. True or False: Francesca Hetfield met her husband James when she was working as a costume designer for Metallica.

10. Who produced Metallica's second album, *Ride the Lightning*?

    a. Jon Zazula

    b. Jake Runestead

    c. Mark Lewis

    d. Fleming Rasmussen

11. When Metallica recorded their first symphonic album with the San Francisco Symphony, what was the name of the composer/arranger they worked with?

    a. Donato Cabrera

    b. Michael Kamen

    c. Alfred Wallenstein

    d. John Williams

12. Who produced the album *Death Magnetic*?

    a. Rick Rubin

    b. Carl Marston

    c. Harris Johns

    d. Bob Rock

13. When James Hetfield broke his wrist in 1986, who filled in on rhythm guitar on their U.S. tour?

a. Scott Ian
b. Mille Petrozza
c. John Marshall
d. Rudolph Schenker

ANSWERS

1. B - Paul Curcio

2. True

3. C - Joe Satriani

4. True

5. A - Deep Purple

6. B - Bob Rock

7. C - Jon Zazula

8. A - Peter Mensch

9. True

10. D - Fleming Rasmussen

11. B - Michael Kamen

12. A - Rick Rubin

13. C - John Marshall

DID YOU KNOW?

- The very first lineup of musicians for Metallica was Lars Ulrich on drums, James Hetfield on vocals and rhythm guitar, Ron McGovny on bass, and Dave Mustaine on lead guitar.

- Ron McGovny and James Hetfield were childhood friends and formed a band called Leather Charm together. After starting and joining Metallica with Lars Ulrich, Dave Mustaine was recruited via a newspaper ad. They all would rehearse in Ron's basement.

- James Hetfield has recorded several great guitar solos on tracks such as "Nothing Else Matters" and the first interlude solo in "Master of Puppets." He and Lars Ulrich have co-written most of Metallica's songs.

- Since 1984, "Big" Mick Hughes has been the live audio engineer for Metallica. He has mixed at every one of Metallica's shows since their November 1984 tour of Europe, with the exception of a couple of shows because he was hospitalized with heart palpitations. Amongst the band, he is known as Full Roar.

- Wayne Isham directed the films *S&M* and *S&M2*, which are live performances of Metallica in collaboration with the San Francisco Symphony.

The first was released in 1999, and the second on the 20th anniversary of the first in 2019.

- The lead single from Metallica's album *Reload*, "The Memory Remains," features British singer and actress Marianne Faithful on backing vocals. She was also featured in the music video for the song.

- Lars Ulrich's father offered opinions and advice about Metallica's music in the studio. A memorable moment caught on camera is during the recording of the album *St. Anger*. After listening to a recording, his blunt advice was to "delete that."

- Cliff Burton had a passion for classical music and was knowledgeable about music theory and songwriting. He shared his knowledge with the band, which helped elevate their music.

- Brian Slagel met Lars Ulrich in Southern California prior to the formation of Metallica, and they became friends. Slagel would go on to found the independent record label that would produce albums featuring Metallica's first official song.

- Alice in Chains guitarist Jerry Cantrell is a close friend of Metallica and has performed with them live a handful of times. In 2020, Cantrell called James Hetfield the "godfather" among rock icons.

CHAPTER 3:

CHANGES TO THE BAND

TRIVIA TIME!

1. Which Metallica song did Robert Trujillo play at his audition for the band that impressed the members of Metallica the most?

    a. "Battery"
    b. "Master of Puppets"
    c. "Ride the Lightning"
    d. "Kill 'Em All"

2. True or False: Metallica is considered a crossover band.

3. Because Jason Newsted left the band, who filled in on bass for the album *St. Anger*?

    a. Bob Rock
    b. Kirk Hammett
    c. Robert Trujillo
    d. David Ellefson

4. True or False: James Hetfield worked with a vocal coach after Metallica's first album, and many fans noticed the change in his voice.

5. To the dismay of many hardcore metal fans, Metallica changed its image by donning shorter haircuts with the promotion and release of which album?

    a. *Metallica*
    b. *Hardwired… To Self-Destruct*
    c. *St. Anger*
    d. *Load*

6. James Hetfield learned to be freer with lyrics during Metallica's collaboration with which music artist?

    a. Ozzy Osbourne
    b. Ja Rule
    c. Lou Reed
    d. AC/DC

7. When Metallica was still forming and recording their first demo, who played lead guitar on the demo version of "Hit the Lights"?

    a. David Mustaine
    b. Lloyd Grant
    c. James Hetfield
    d. Kirk Hammett

8. True or False: In 2020, Metallica started working on an orchestral version of their song "Nothing Else Matters" for a Marvel movie collaboration.

9. While Metallica's first concert hosted around two hundred people, their biggest concert to date brought around how many fans to the crowd?

a. 1.6 million
b. 1 million
c. 760,000
d. 540,000

10. Although they began as a thrash metal band, what genre is Metallica overall considered to be now?

   a. Country Rock
   b. Classic Rock
   c. Heavy Metal
   d. Death Metal

11. True or False: In the beginning, James Hetfield focused on singing and did not play guitar for Metallica's first few shows.

12. While James Hetfield is the frontman for Metallica, which band member did the band consider making frontman at the beginning because of James' shyness?

   a. Lars Ulrich
   b. David Mustaine
   c. Ron McGovny
   d. Cliff Burton

13. Which former member of Metallica claimed to have left the band because of "private and personal reasons and the physical damage I have done to myself over the years while playing the music that I love."

   a. Ron McGovney
   b. Jason Newsted

c. Dave Mustaine
d. Cliff Burton

ANSWERS

1. A - "Battery"

2. True

3. A - Bob Rock

4. False - That happened after the third album.

5. D - *Load*

6. C - Lou Reed

7. B - Lloyd Grant

8. False - For a Disney movie collaboration

9. A - 1.6 million

10. C - Heavy Metal

11. True

12. A - Lars Ulrich

13. B - Jason Newsted

DID YOU KNOW?

- Although Metallica was founded in Los Angeles, they relocated to the San Francisco area in order to recruit bass player Cliff Burton. Cliff agreed to join the band on the condition that they come to him, and he was based near San Francisco.

- At their peak, Metallica incorporated themes of abuse of power, control, and expressions of anti-war sentiment. Themes of political and legal injustices and corruption were written into their music in the late 1980s. Subsequent albums gained mainstream attention and exposure, and Metallica strayed away from their thrash metal roots to explore more of an alt-rock style.

- The album *St. Anger* brought a new era full of changes to Metallica and their music. An instrumental alteration in the recordings is heard with, Lars Ulrich's snare drum having what bitter fans have described as "trash can drums." He had turned the metal snares off or loosened them to create a hollower tone.

- When writing songs initially, little collaboration occurred between the band members: with James Hetfield controlling most, if not all, of the lyrical content. This led to some resentment and struggles for power between the members of the band. In an attempt to resolve the division between the members, a new approach was taken with writing and recording the album *St. Anger*. Metallica wrote music for the album together, writing music and lyrics collaboratively in a stream of consciousness approach.

- Metallica brought themselves out of their lull following James Hetfield's stint in rehab by putting themselves on a schedule of noon-4pm. This aligned with Hetfield's recovery schedule following rehabilitation for addiction and was the first time the band had really adhered to a schedule.

- Robert Trujillo and Jason Newsted basically swapped bands. When Trujillo left Ozzy Osbourne to join Metallica, Newsted became his replacement in Ozzy's band.

CHAPTER 4:

ALBUMS AND RECORD DEALS

TRIVIA TIME!

1. Founded in 1982, what was the name of the first record label to sign Metallica and publish their first works?
    a. Blackened Records
    b. Elektra Records
    c. Megaforce Records
    d. Metalmania Records

2. In what city was Metallica's debut album recorded?
    a. Los Angeles
    b. San Francisco
    c. Chicago
    d. Rochester

3. What is the name of the studio in Copenhagen, Denmark, where Metallica recorded two albums, *Ride the Lightning* and *Master of Puppets*?
    a. Sweet Silence Studios
    b. Ocean Sound Recording
    c. Black Tornado Studio
    d. Medley Studios

4. True or False: Metallica's album titled *Kill 'Em All* was not the originally-chosen name but had to be renamed at their distributor's request at the time.

5. Which Metallica album was the first to reach gold certification and later went platinum?

    a. *Ride the Lightning*
    b. *Kill 'Em All*
    c. *Master of Puppets*
    d. *...And Justice for All*

6. Considered their "come-back" album, which Metallica album was also said to have compromised the sound quality and was criticized as over-compressed?

    a. *Kill 'Em All*
    b. *St. Anger*
    c. *Death Magnetic*
    d. *Hardwired... To Self-Destruct*

7. Launched in 2012, what is the name of Metallica's self-owned record label?

    a. Blackened Records
    b. Metallica Records
    c. Master Records
    d. One Records

8. True or False: At first, Metallica struggled to secure a record label, so John Zazula created one for them.

9. Which Metallica album became the first metal recording selected by the Library of Congress for

preservation in the National Recording Registry for being "culturally, historically, or aesthetically significant"?

   a. *Metallica*
   b. *Ride the Lightning*
   c. *Garage, Inc.*
   d. *Master of Puppets*

10. Going for a raw, stripped down sound, which Metallica album was aimed at sounding more like a garage band and was purposely less polished-sounding?

   a. *Garage, Inc.*
   b. *Death Magnetic*
   c. *Hardwired... To Self-Destruct*
   d. *St. Anger*

11. True or False: The album *Death Magnetic* did not feature any guitar solos.

12. In what city was Metallica's fourth album, *...And Justice for All*, recorded?

   a. New York City, New York
   b. Copenhagen, Denmark
   c. Los Angeles, California
   d. San Francisco, California

13. True or False: *Hardwired... To Self-Destruct* is Metallica's tenth studio album.

ANSWERS

1. C - Megaforce Records

2. D - Rochester

3. A - Sweet Silence Studios

4. True - The original name was Metal Up Your Ass.

5. C - *Master of Puppets*

6. C - Death Magnetic

7. A - Blackened Records

8. True

9. D - *Master of Puppets*

10. D - *St. Anger*

11. False - The album *St. Anger* had no guitar solos.

12. C - Los Angeles, California

13. True

DID YOU KNOW?

- After hearing *Ride the Lightning*, Elektra Records signed Metallica and then, in 1986, released the group's third studio album, *Master of Puppets.* Hailed as Metallica's masterpiece, Metallica opted to go straight to touring with this album rather than release a single or video to promote the album.

- Released in 1988 by Elektra Records, Metallica's album *...And Justice for All* was the first to feature new bassist Jason Newsted. Unfortunately, though, the bass was turned down in the final mixing and is hardly audible throughout the album.

- As Metallica reached a more mainstream audience, they continued to experiment with their music and sound. Released in 1996, *Load,* to some fans' dismay, is more of a hard rock album rather than metal, which was new for Metallica. Influences from Southern rock, blues rock, alt-rock, and country rock are heard throughout, leaving their thrash metal roots. Despite the criticism from their fanbase, *Load* was a commercial success.

- One year later, the follow-up to *Load* was released as *Reload.* It contained songs that were not completed in time for its predecessor and were in line with the hard rock approach of the album. The idea had been to release them as a double album, but the group decided it would be better to split up the materials. *Reload* was also met with criticism by Metallica's fanbase but debuted at No. 1 on the Billboard 200.

- *St. Anger* was released in 2003 and was the last album released through Elektra Records with producer Bob Rock.

- The first album to be released on their record label Blackened, *Hardwired... to Self-Destruct* was released as a double album in 2016. It debuted at No. 1 on the Billboard Hot 200, making it Metallica's sixth consecutive studio album to do so.

CHAPTER 5:

SONGS

TRIVIA TIME!

1. Metallica's album *Ride the Lightning* closed with an almost nine-minute-long instrumental track titled what?
    a. "The Ecstasy of Gold"
    b. "The Call of Ktulu"
    c. "My Friend of Misery"
    d. "To Live Is To Die"

2. Which song was Metallica's first top 40 hit in the U.S.?
    a. "War Pigs"
    b. "Fade to Black"
    c. "One"
    d. "Welcome Home (Sanitarium)"

3. Which of the following was Metallica's first recorded original song?
    a. "Whiplash"
    b. "Hit the Lights"
    c. "Am I Evil?"
    d. "The Four Horsemen"

4. True or False: James Hetfield wrote the song "The God That Failed" in reference to his Christian Scientist parents.

5. At 11:10, Metallica's longest track is a mix of five songs by what Danish heavy metal band?

    a. Force of Evil
    b. Pretty Maids
    c. Konkhra
    d. Mercyful Fate

6. Lars Ulrich described which Metallica hit as a "one-riff" song, which would become their biggest hit?

    a. "Enter Sandman"
    b. "Master of Puppets"
    c. "Blackened"
    d. "Wherever I May Roam"

7. On their album ...And Justice for All, Metallica wrote which song as a tribute to deceased bassist Cliff Burton?

    a. "To Live is To Die"
    b. "That Was Just Your Life"
    c. "The Day That Never Comes"
    d. "Turn the Page"

8. True or False: "Sad But True" sounds extra heavy because the guitars were tuned down to D and cranked up.

9. What were the unreleased recording sessions for the album *Death Magnetic* titled and released as an E.P.?

    a. *Mega Magnetic*
    b. *Magnetic Plus*
    c. *Beyond Magnetic*
    d. *Alive Magnetic*

10. What song did Metallica perform with Lady Gaga at the 59th Grammy Awards in 2017?

    a. "Halo on Fire"
    b. "Moth into Flame"
    c. "Dream No More"
    d. "Here Comes Revenge"

11. True or False: The title track "Master of Puppets" was used as the official theme song for WWE's SummerSlam 2003.

12. Which Metallica song is a tribute to a favorite stomping ground, the Old Waldorf club in San Francisco?

    a. "Damage Inc."
    b. "Battery"
    c. "King Nothing"
    d. "Ronnie"

13. Featuring the sounds of acoustic guitar for the first time on a Metallica album, what song was considered to be their first "slow song"?

    a. "Nothing Else Matters"

b. "Fade to Black"

c. "One"

d. "Sad But True"

14. It's tradition for Metallica to end a show with which song?

   a. "For Whom the Bell Tolls"

   b. "Escape"

   c. "Seek and Destroy"

   d. "Whiskey in the Jar"

15. Constantly shifting time signatures throughout, which Metallica song was uncharacteristically political, about the "death of mother earth" and the threat of nuclear war?

   a. "Master of Puppets"

   b. "My Apocalypse"

   c. "Fuel"

   d. "Blackened"

16. True or False: "Harvester of Sorrow" shares its title with an Ernest Hemingway novel book from 1940.

17. What was the first single from Metallica's debut album, *Kill 'Em All*?

   a. "Hit the Lights"

   b. "Motorbreath"

   c. "The Four Horsemen"

   d. "Whiplash"

18. What is Metallica's most-played song, having been performed over 1,600 times?

a. "Ride the Lightning"
b. "Master of Puppets"
c. "Seek and Destroy"
d. "Creeping Death"

ANSWERS

1. B - "The Call of Ktulu"

2. C - "One"

3. B - "Hit the Lights"

4. True

5. D - Mercyful Fate

6. A - "Enter Sandman"

7. A - "To Live is To Die"

8. True

9. C - *Beyond Magnetic*

10. B - "Moth Into Flame"

11. False - "St. Anger" was the track.

12. B - "Battery"

13. B - "Fade to Black"

14. C - "Seek and Destroy"

15. D - "Blackened"

16. False - "For Whom the Bell Tolls" shares its title with a Hemingway novel.

17. D - "Whiplash"

18. B - "Master of Puppets"

DID YOU KNOW?

- Released as the third and final single for the album *...And Justice for All*, "One" is considered to be Metallica's anti-war anthem. It portrays a World War I soldier who has lost his arms and legs, is blind and unable to speak or move, and is wishing for the end of his life.

- Metallica's second-ever ballad is a dark tale of a man trapped in an asylum, titled "Welcome Home (Sanitarium)."

- Full of references from the *Book of Exodus*, "Creeping Death" is a song told from the point of view of the Angel of Death. The title and lyrical content were inspired after Metallica watched a scene from the Charlton Heston movie *The Ten Commandments* where the Angel of Death kills the first-born sons of Egypt.

- The song "Whiskey in The Jar" was not originally written by Metallica but is an Irish folk song. Metallica's version is a cover of the arrangement recorded by Irish hard rock band Thin Lizzy.

- Metallica wrote a trilogy referred to as The Unforgiven Trilogy, consisting of the songs "The Unforgiven," "The Unforgiven II," and "The Unforgiven III." The theme and story being continued in each of them.

- The main riff "To Live Is to Die" was written by Cliff Burton, along with half of its lyrics. It was written while Metallica was writing *Master of Puppets* but didn't make it on the album due to space constraints. The last line of the song, "Cannot the kingdom of salvation take me home?" is etched on Cliff's memorial stone in Sweden.

- James Hetfield started writing the song "Nothing Else Matters" about his feelings for his girlfriend at the time, but he had no intention of releasing it on a Metallica album. Lars Ulrich convinced him that it belonged on an album, so it was recorded on *The Black Album*. It has become a staple in their live performances as a dedication to their fans.

- The song title "Ride the Lightning" came from the Stephen King novel *The Stand*. Kirk Hammet came across the line when reading the portion of the novel about a man on death row facing the electric chair.

- The lead single of the album *Load,* "Until It Sleeps," was the band's first No. 1 on the U.S. Billboard Hot Mainstream Rock Tracks chart and is also their first song as of their tenth album to hit the top ten of the Billboard Hot 100.

- Metallica's song "I Disappear" was written for the movie *Mission Impossible II* in 2000. Actor Tom Cruise personally convinced Metallica to record the soundtrack by showing them footage of the film in action.

CHAPTER 6:

FAMOUS MOMENTS

TRIVIA TIME!

1. After almost three years of touring to promote the album *Metallica*, Metallica was one of the headliners for which festival in 1994?

    a. Rockfest '94
    b. Woodstock '94
    c. MetalMania '94
    d. Electric Forest Festival '94

2. In the summer of 1991, Metallica hosted the "world's largest album listening party" for *The Black Album* at what location?

    a. Wrigley Field
    b. Staples Center
    c. Madison Square Gardens
    d. Fenway Park

3. True or False: During his first show with Metallica, Kirk Hammett had his guitar taken by the crowd, and it had to be recovered by the guitar techs working for the band.

4. What did the sticker on James Hetfield's 1985 Jackson King V Custom guitar say?

    a. Get 'Em
    b. Dark Deets
    c. Bring Beer
    d. Kill Bon Jovi

5. Lemmy Kilmister from Motorhead joined Metallica, who were big fans of Motorhead, in 1996 to perform, and James Hetfield returned the favor, appearing with Motorhead in 2000. In both instances, what song did they perform?

    a. "Ace of Spades"
    b. "Overkill"
    c. "Killed by Death"
    d. "No Class"

6. True or False: Metallica headlined Lollapalooza in 1991.

7. In 2012, Metallica planned and headlined a two-day festival in its inaugural year called what?

    a. Blackened Music + More
    b. Orion Music + More
    c. Metallica Music + More
    d. Frantic Music + More

8. True or False: The first tour in which the band used live recordings of their concerts in single B-sides and E.P.'s was the Damaged Justice tour.

9. How many nights did Metallica pack the Fillmore in San Francisco for their thirtieth anniversary in 2011?

   a. Three
   b. Four
   c. Five
   d. Six

10. In 2008, Metallica returned to their basement roots with a performance in the basement of what Nashville record store?

    a. Grimey's
    b. The Great Escape
    c. The Groove
    d. Vinyl Tap

11. True or False: Metallica was the first-ever metal band to headline for the Glastonbury Festival.

12. Who did Metallica perform their song "One" with at the 56th Annual Grammy Awards?

    a. Pianist Lang Lang
    b. Cellist Yo Yo Ma
    c. Violinist Itzhak Perlman
    d. Harpist Yolanda Kondonassis

13. In June of 2019, Metallica famously played for nearly two and a half hours at what location in Ireland?

    a. Slane Castle
    b. The Blarney Castle
    c. The Cliffs of Moher

d. The Rock of Cashel

14. True or False: In their early years, Metallica was defiant about going commercial and refused to make music videos.

15. One of the biggest concerts in the history of rock and roll, including Metallica, went down at the Monsters of Rock Festival at Tushino Airfield in Moscow in what year?

   a. 1989
   b. 1990
   c. 1991
   d. 1992

16. Which member of Metallica appeared before the Senate Judiciary Committee in 2000 to provide a statement about the future of the internet and copyright issues?

   a. Kirk Hammett
   b. Jason Newsted
   c. James Hetfield
   d. Lars Ulrich

17. True or False: The release of Metallica's album …*And Justice For All* made the band stadium headliners.

18. In what year did Metallica headline the Monsters of Rock Festival, but only under the condition that it be called Escape from the Studio?

   a. 1995

b. 1993

c. 1991

d. 1987

19. While recording *The Black Album*, Lars Ulrich was filmed throwing darts at a poster of what rock singer?

a. Bon Jovi

b. Kip Winger

c. Vince Neil

d. Axl Rose

ANSWERS

1. B - Woodstock '94

2. C - Madison Square Gardens

3. True

4. D - Kill Bon Jovi

5. B - Overkill

6. False - Metallica headlined Lollapalooza in 1996.

7. B - Orion Music + More

8. True

9. B - Four

10. A - Grimey's

11. True

12. A - Pianist Lang Lang

13. A - Slane Castle

14. True

15. C - 1991

16. D - Lars Ulrich

17. False - *The Black Album* made them stadium headliners.

18. A - 1995

19. B - Kip Winger

DID YOU KNOW?

- In anticipation of Metallica's performance at the MTV Europe Music Awards, MTV officials approached the band to inform them that no expletives were allowed. Instead of their planned song, "King Nothing," Metallica changed their set that day to two songs packed with offensive material, "Last Caress" by the Misfits and "So What?" by the Anti-Nowhere League.

- The Big Four, containing Metallica, Megadeth, Slayer, and Anthrax, came together in 2010 for the first time to perform in Warsaw, Poland. It was such a success that The Big Four would go on to play several more shows across the globe together.

- In August of 2020, Metallica performed for a drive-in concert that showed in theaters across America. They were the first rock band to be featured in the Encore Drive-In Nights series. Every ticket purchase admitted one carload of up to six people.

- A Day on the Green Concert of 1985 was a landmark performance for Metallica to gain media attention and perform for a large stadium audience. Although The Scorpions and Ratt were the top-billed bands that year, pro footage of Metallica also appeared on MTV, giving them their first mainstream media exposure.

- There have been a few occasions where Metallica has needed to perform with substitutes for its members. When James Hetfield suffered a back injury from a skiing accident in 2000, several musicians from the other bands on the tour filled in to sing for three shows. Musicians included Jonathan Davis and Fieldy from Korn, Serj Tankien from System of a Down, and Kid Rock with his rapper partner Joe C.

- In 2004, Lars Ulrich fell ill right before Metallica's performance for the Download tour, so Slipknot's Joey Jordison, Slayer's Dave Lombardo, and roadie Flemming Larsen played the drums for Metallica throughout the show.

- During a collaborative Grammy performance with Lady Gaga and Metallica in 2017, James Hetfield's microphone was unplugged or shut off. Lady Gaga shared her microphone for the performance, but unfortunately, it all played out on a live broadcast.

- In 2013, Metallica began a regular engagement with the San Francisco Giants baseball team. They staged a Metallica-themed night with activities and events during a Giants game, including the playing of the national anthem by Hetfield and Hammett for the first time in their careers. The baseball team has since held "Metallica Night" annually.

- In celebration of Motorhead frontman, Lemmy Kilmister's, 50th birthday in 1995, Metallica took the stage at the Whiskey a Go Go as The Lemmys, posing as a Motorhead tribute band. As The Lemmys, they wore wigs and regalia to imitate the singer's appearance.

CHAPTER 7:

TOURS & LIVE SHOWS

TRIVIA TIME!

1. What Metallica song was most requested on the Metallica By Request Tour?

    a. "Master of Puppets"
    b. "Seek and Destroy"
    c. "Fuel"
    d. "Enter Sandman"

2. True or False: The name of Metallica's first major headlining tour as a band, supporting their first album, was called the Kill 'Em All for One tour.

3. Which English metal band did Metallica play as a supporting act for on the Seven Dates of Hell tour?

    a. Napalm Death
    b. Onslaught
    c. Venom
    d. Angel Witch

4. True or False: In their first major European tour, the band played to an average crowd of over 5,000 people.

5. On their next tour, the Ride the Lightning Tour, how big was the largest crowd the band played for?

    a. 20,000 people
    b. 50,000 people
    c. 70,000 people
    d. 100,000 people

6. The crumbling centerpiece of Metallica's ...*And Justice For All Tour's* stage set was a depiction of Lady Justice from the album cover, who Metallica gave what nickname?

    a. Doris
    b. Dorothy
    c. Diana
    d. Darcey

7. On their second festival tour, Monsters of Rock '87, the group performed in Donington Castle, England, the usual venue for the festival. Where else did the group perform on this tour?

    a. France
    b. The U.S.A.
    c. Canada
    d. West Germany

8. True or False: The next year, Metallica went on the same festival tour, and again they were the headliner of the tour.

9. True or False: On Tour 1990, the group played a secret show at The Marquee supporting Metal Church.

10. On their fourth festival tour, the last concert, held on September 28th, was described as "the first free outdoor Western rock concert in Soviet history" Where did this last concert take place?

    a. Kizhi Island, Karelia
    b. Tushino Airfield, Moscow
    c. St. Sophia Cathedral, Novgorod
    d. Hermitage Museum, St. Petersburg

11. In what year did Metallica first headline at Wembley Stadium?

    a. 1989
    b. 1995
    c. 2000
    d. 2007

12. On the Wherever We May Roam Tour, which supported the band's fifth album, *Metallica*, the group performed at a tribute concert for which well-known artist?

    a. Michael Jackson
    b. Jimi Hendrix
    c. Freddie Mercury
    d. Elton John

13. True or False: On the group's tour following Wherever We May Roam, Metallica was the only headliner.

14. True or False: Metallica's tour following the Nowhere Else to Roam tour included a performance at Woodstock '94, in front of over 350,000 people.

15. In the Escape from the Studio '95 tour, Metallica played a song from their two next albums. One of the albums was called *2 x 4*. What was the name of the other album?

    a. *The Black Album*
    b. *Metallica*
    c. *Devil's Dance*
    d. *Master of Puppets*

16. True or False: Metallica was not the headliner for festival tour Lollapalooza No. 6.

17. Which tour saw the band performing only cover songs, with the opening acts being Metallica cover bands?

    a. Garage Inc Promo Tour
    b. Poor Re-Touring Me Tour
    c. Re-load Promo Tour
    d. Blitzkrieg '97

18. True or False: Metallica's M2K Mini Tour included a New Year's Eve show, in Pontiac, Michigan.

ANSWERS

1. A - *Master of Puppets*

2. True

3. C - Venom

4. False - The average was only about 1,300 people per show.

5. C - 70,000 people

6. A - Doris

7. D – West Germany

8. False - Iron Maiden headlined the main Monsters of Rock show the following year.

9. True

10. Tushino Airfield, Moscow

11. D - 2007

12. C - Freddie Mercury

13. False - In this tour, Guns N' Roses was a co-headliner on part of the tour.

14. True

15. C - Devil's Dance

16. False - Metallica was the headliner.

17. A - Garage Inc. Promo Tour

18. True

DID YOU KNOW?

- As of early 2021, Metallica has been on a total of seven worldwide tours: Damage Inc. Tour, Damaged Justice, Wherever We May Roam Tour, Nowhere Else to Roam, Madly in Anger with the World Tour, Escape from the Studio '96, and World Magnetic Tour.

- The first show of the Guns N' Roses/Metallica Stadium Tour was played at R.F.K. stadium, where the band recorded their song "Creeping Death" for the documentary, *A Year and a Half in the Life of Metallica.*

- After the release of the album *Master of Puppets* in 1986, Metallica went on tour with Ozzy Osbourne, and unfortunately, this tour was one that ended in the death of bassist Cliff Burton.

- The Wherever We May Roam tour in support of *The Black Album* lasted for three years. It spanned the globe, with 224 shows performed.

- Metallica famously sold Snake Pit tickets during their tour promoting *The Black Album.* The Snake Pit was a special area near the stage that held 150-200 fans. It has been used on and off through the years of live shows and tours.

- The Monsters of Rock concert, played at Tushino Airfield in Moscow, included Metallica and was one of the highest-attendance music concerts in history, with an estimated total of over 1.6 million people attending.

- The band first played at the Monsters of Rock festival during their Ride the Lightning tour, in one of their last, best shows with Cliff Burton. This performance took place in front of a crowd of over 70,000 people, the largest crowd the band had seen up to this point.

- Metallica's Blitzkrieg '97 tour only happened to fulfill previous contractual obligations. They were required to play a set number of shows at European festivals, including an appearance at the Pukkelpop Festival in Belgium.

CHAPTER 8:

HARDSHIP AND CONTROVERSY

TRIVIA TIME!

1. Which Metallica song led to Metallica's discovery and subsequent suing of Napster?

    a. "All Nightmare Long"
    b. "Enter Sandman"
    c. "I Disappear"
    d. "Whiskey in the Jar"

2. James Hetfield suffered second-degree burns to his arms, legs, face, and hands, and third-degree burns on his arms, when he walked into a 12-foot flame during which tour?

    a. Guns N' Roses/Metallica Stadium Tour
    b. Wherever We May Roam Tour
    c. Monsters of Rock '91
    d. Escape from the Studio '95

3. Titled as "The Four Horsemen" on Metallica's album *Kill 'Em All*, Dave Mustaine, who had writing credits for the song, released a speeded-up Megadeth version of the same song under what alternate song title?

a. "Phantom Lord"
b. "Wake Up Dead"
c. "Take No Prisoners"
d. "The Mechanix"

4. In an effort to salvage the band and continue making music, Metallica hired who as their Performance Enhancement Coach in 2001?

   a. Paddy Steinfort
   b. Phil Towle
   c. John Kenyon
   d. Eric Paulson

5. Who was Lars Ulrich's personal assistant from 2001-2009 that sued him for unpaid wages?

   a. Barbara Dane
   b. Emma White
   c. Mark Yearling
   d. Steve Wiig

6. True or False: The back of the album *Load* features a photo of Metallica with short hair, eye makeup, Cuban suits, and cigars.

7. Which member of Metallica lost his phone in 2015 that contained hundreds of song ideas for the band's 10th record?

   a. James Hetfield
   b. Robert Trujillo
   c. Kirk Hammett
   d. Lars Ulrich

8. When the band was uncertain of their future, James wrote and released a heartfelt, handwritten note in a METALLICA Club fan publication called what?

    a. *So What!*
    b. *Who Cares!*
    c. *Yeah Right!*
    d. *Oh Yeah!*

9. Which member of Metallica was honored at the 2006 MusiCares M.A.P. Fund benefit concert?

    a. Jason Newsted
    b. Kirk Hammett
    c. James Hetfield
    d. Lars Ulrich

10. True or False: It is reported that over fifty people died at the Monsters of Rock concert in Russia in 1991.

11. Which Metallica album leaked ten days before its release?

    a. *Reload*
    b. *Hardwired... To Self-Destruct!*
    c. *Metallica*
    d. *Death Magnetic*

12. Former Metallica member Jason Newsted left the band to make music with his own band, called what?

    a. Bloodreverb
    b. Echobrain

    c. Flasheye

    d. Nosebleed

13. In what year was the tragic tour bus accident that resulted in the death of Metallica bassist Cliff Burton?

    a. 1983

    b. 1984

    c. 1985

    d. 1986

14. What was the name of the flash cartoon series created under the Camp Chaos banner that mocked Metallica for its role in the Napster controversy?

    a. *Napster Bad!*

    b. *Naughty Napster!*

    c. *Napster Good!*

    d. *No No Napster!*

15. True or False: Metallica frontman James Hetfield supported the legal defense and release of the West Memphis Three.

16. What Metallica song is considered to be their most controversial because of both its address of suicidal thoughts and acoustic sounds?

    a. "Nothing Else Matters"

    b. "Fight Fire with Fire"

    c. "The Unforgiven"

    d. "Fade to Black"

ANSWERS

1. C - "I Disappear"

2. A - Guns N' Roses/Metallica Stadium Tour

3. D - "The Mechanix"

4. B - Phil Towle

5. D - Steve Wiig

6. True

7. C - Kirk Hammett

8. A - *So What!*

9. C - James Hetfield

10. True

11. D - *Death Magnetic*

12. B - Echobrain

13. D - 1986

14. A - *Napster Bad!*

15. True

16. D – "Fade to Black"

DID YOU KNOW?

- Metallica's bassist from 1983-1986, Cliff Burton, tragically died when the band's tour bus crashed on September 27, 1986. Earlier that night, he and Kirk Hammett drew cards over who would sleep in the bunk with the window. Cliff drew the Ace of Spades and called dibs on Kirk's bunk with the window. He was later ejected from the bus through that window and crushed by the bus.

- Metallica notoriously had over 300,000 Napster users kicked off the platform during their legal assault against the file-sharing service. They spent most of the year 2000 in controversy over copyright infringement, sparking debates of the availability of digital music. In 2001, they reached a settlement and, Napster became a pay-to-access service.

- A lot of rumors have circulated about the lack of bass guitar sound throughout the album *...And Justice for All*. At the time, bass guitarist Jason Newsted was hazed frequently by the band, so for a while, it was believed that his part was turned down intentionally in the final mixing to bully or spite him. Lars Ulrich and James Hetfield have claimed that it was not intentional since then, blaming their fried ears for turning the highs up so much that the lows were drowned out during the mixing process.

- In 1994, Metallica sued their record label at the time, Elektra Records, in an effort to get out of their contract with them. Metallica felt they were not fairly compensated. The C.E.O. of eleven years, Robert Krasnow, had made a verbal agreement to increase the band's royalties; however, he was on his way out, and Warner Music was taking over. Metallica pursued a lawsuit in an effort to force their label's hand, and the label and band later settled an agreement.

- After having their gear stolen, including his favorite Marshall amplifier, in 1984, James Hetfield was feeling depressed and wrote the song "Fade to Black."

- After working with a therapist on and off for two years, Metallica was not pleased with his presence any longer. They felt he was overstepping and trying to be a part of the band, so they pushed for ending their sessions, at least temporarily.

- James Hetfield's love for hunting led to protests to have Metallica removed from the lineup of 2017's Glastonbury Festival. The announcement of the History Channel's show *Hunt* ignited the uproar because James narrated the series about bear hunting in Alaska. Many felt that James' support of the show and big-game hunting was not compatible with the spirit of Glastonbury.

- In his biography, guitarist Scott Ian from Anthrax wrote about Metallica's plans to fire Lars Ulrich in 1986, prior to Cliff Burton's death. Lars was unaware of the comments made by his bandmates until after the biography was shared by Scott Ian in 2014.

CHAPTER 9:

MUSIC VIDEOS, T.V. AND FILM

TRIVIA TIME!

1. To commemorate the life of band member Cliff Burton, Metallica released a video album titled what?

   a. *Ode to Cliff*
   b. *Remembering Cliff*
   c. *Cliff 'Em All*
   d. *Cliff and Country*

2. Featuring Metallica performing along with a fictional thriller storyline, what was the name of the concert film that the band wrote the screenplay for?

   a. *Metallica: Some Kind of Monster*
   b. *Metallica: Through the Never*
   c. *2 of One*
   d. *S&M*

3. Which member of Metallica made a cameo appearance in the comedic film *Get Him to the Greek*?

   a. James Hetfield
   b. Lars Ulrich
   c. Kirk Hammett

    d. Robert Trujillo

4. True or False: Metallica made a music video for every song on their album *Death Magnetic.*

5. The music video for the song "St. Anger" was shot at what location?

    a. San Antonio Winery
    b. San Quentin California State Prison
    c. Rainbow Bar and Grill in Los Angeles, California
    d. The Golden Gate Bridge

6. Metallica's first music video was for which song?

    a. "…And Justice For All"
    b. "Blackened"
    c. "Harvester of Sorrow"
    d. "One"

7. What is the title of the Metallica documentary that was filmed while the group was recording their eponymous album, *Metallica*?

    a. *A Year and a Half in the Life of Metallica*
    b. *Metallica: The Black Album*
    c. *Metal World Domination*
    d. *Metallica: Some Kind of Monster*

8. True or False: The music video for the song "Fuel" has nothing to do with cars.

9. Uncredited, James Hetfield sang backing vocals for which song from the film *South Park: Bigger, Longer, and Uncut*?

   a. "Blame Canada"
   b. "Hell Isn't Good"
   c. "The Mole's Reprise"
   d. "Wendy's Song"

10. In the music video for the Metallica song "One," footage of the members playing in a giant warehouse is spliced together with parts of what 1971 film?

    a. *Willy Wonka and the Chocolate Factory*
    b. *Dirty Harry*
    c. *Johnny Got His Gun*
    d. *Escape from the Planet of the Apes*

11. Who does James Hetfield play in Netflix's 2019 movie *Extremely Wicked, Shockingly Evil & Vile*, a biopic about Ted Bundy?

    a. Bob Hayward
    b. David Lee
    c. Mike Minerva
    d. Edward Cowert

12. True or False: The music video for "For Whom the Bell Tolls" is military-themed.

13. Which Metallica song has a music video set in the Middle Eastern desert with a group of marines?

    a. "One"

b. "Fade to Black"

c. "The Unforgiven"

d. "The Day That Never Comes"

14. A trusted visual collaborator by the likes of U2 and Depeche Mode, who also directed the Metallica music video for "Hero of The Day?"

a. Anton Corbijn

b. Wayne Isham

c. Adam Dubin

d. Michael Lindsey

15. Which Metallica music video tells the story of a child growing to old age while chipping away at his stone cell?

a. "Nothing Else Matters"

b. "All Nightmare Long"

c. "The Unforgiven"

d. "…And Justice For All"

16. Done in a mockumentary style, which Metallica song has a music video of fictional historical events involving a bioweapon and a zombie apocalypse?

a. "All Nightmare Long"

b. "Wherever I May Roam"

c. "Seek & Destroy"

d. "Moth Into Flame"

17. Which Metallica music video features footage from the documentary *A Year and a Half in the Life of Metallica*?

a. "Nothing Else Matters"
b. "Blackened"
c. "Enter Sandman"
d. "Wherever I May Roam"

18. What city was the music video for "King Nothing" filmed?

   a. Vancouver, Canada
   b. Park City, Utah
   c. Mexico City, Mexico
   d. Los Angeles, California

19. Metallica collaborated with Swizz Beatz and Ja Rule to record a song called "We Did It Again" for what film?

   a. *School of Rock*
   b. *Hulk*
   c. *Holes*
   d. *Biker Boyz*

ANSWERS

1. C - *Cliff 'Em All*

2. B - *Metallica: Through the Never*

3. B - Lars Ulrich

4. False - *Hardwired… To Self-Destruct* was released with music videos for every song.

5. B - San Quentin California State Prison

6. D - "One"

7. A - *A Year and a Half in the Life of Metallica*

8. False - There are many hot rod cars featured.

9. B - "Hell Isn't Good"

10. C - *Johnny Got His Gun*

11. A - Bob Hayward

12. True

13. D - "The Day That Never Comes"

14. A - Anton Corbijn

15. C - "The Unforgiven"

16. A - "All Nightmare Long"

17. A - "Nothing Else Matters"

18. B - Park City, Utah

19. D - *Biker Boyz*

DID YOU KNOW?

- Metallica's first documentary film, *Metallica: Some Kind of Monster,* was released in 2004, then re-released in 2014 for its 10th anniversary. It detailed the making of their album *St. Anger* featuring studio rehearsals and concert footage. It won the "Independent Spirit Award for Best Documentary Feature" in 2005.

- In 2006, Metallica made an appearance as animated versions of themselves in an episode of *The Simpsons* called "The Mook, The Chef and Her Homer."

- James Hetfield made an additional animated cameo in the show *American Dad*, not as himself, but as a water polo coach with his name, appearance, tattoos, and guitars.

- In 2003, MTV selected Metallica to be the subject of its annual tribute show honoring rock legends called ICON.

- The 1967 Chevrolet Camaro driven by James Hetfield in the music video for "I Disappear" was given to him after filming. In 2003, he listed it on eBay, and proceeds from the sale went to music education programs.

- The music video for Metallica's "Turn the Page" has an unexpected story. While the song, originally recorded by Bob Seeger, is about life on the road, the music video tells a troubling life story about a sex worker and her daughter.

- In 2016, Lars Ulrich and James Hetfield made a cameo in the Showtime series *Billions*.

- Fans of the show, James Hetfield and Kirk Hammett voice acted for the Adult Swim network show *Metalocalypse*. Hetfield voiced the character Lorkey the Sailor, and Hammett voiced the Queen of Denmark for several episodes.

- Lars Ulrich raised $32,000 for the Haight Ashbury Free Clinic during his appearance on the celebrity edition of *Who Wants to Be a Millionaire* in 2001.

CHAPTER 10:

AWARDS AND HONORS

TRIVIA TIME!

1. In what year was Metallica inducted into the Rock and Roll Hall of Fame?
   a. 2007
   b. 2009
   c. 2011
   d. 2013

2. In 1988, Metallica was nominated for their first Grammy Award but lost to who, which caused one of the biggest fan upsets in Grammy history?
   a. Yes
   b. Emerson, Lake, and Palmer
   c. Genesis
   d. Jethro Tull

3. Metallica won their first Grammy Award for "Best Metal Performance" for what song for 1989?
   a. "One"
   b. "…And Justice For All"
   c. "Blackened"
   d. "Harvester of Sorrow"

4. At the 33rd Annual Grammy Awards in 1990, Metallica won "Best Metal Performance" with what song?

    a. "Stone Cold Crazy"
    b. "So What"
    c. "Overkill"
    d. "Blitzkrieg"

5. True or False: The album ...*And Justice For All* was Metallica's first Grammy win for an album.

6. Metallica won a Grammy Award for "Best Metal Performance" for what song in 1998?

    a. "The Unforgiven II"
    b. "Fuel"
    c. "Better Than You"
    d. "The Memory Remains"

7. Metallica's cover "Whiskey in the Jar" won a Grammy Award in 1999 under what category?

    a. Best Metal Performance
    b. Best Hard Rock Performance
    c. Best Metal Song
    d. Best Rock Song

8. "The Call of Ktulu" won Metallica a Grammy for "Best Rock Instrumental Performance" in what year?

    a. 1989
    b. 1993

c. 1997

d. 2000

9. True or False: Metallica's album *Hardwired... To Self-Destruct* won the Grammy for Best Rock Album of 2016.

10. The Grammy for "Best Metal Performance" for 2003 went to Metallica for what song?

   a. "Some Kind of Monster"
   b. "St. Anger"
   c. "All Within My Hands"
   d. "My World"

11. The song "My Apocalypse" won Metallica a Grammy for "Best Metal Performance" for what year?

   a. 2004
   b. 2008
   c. 2009
   d. 2011

12. True or False: The song "The Unforgiven III" won Metallica a Grammy Award for "Best Hard Rock Performance".

13. As of the end of 2020, Metallica has won how many American Music Awards for Favorite Heavy Metal/Rock Artist?

   a. 2
   b. 3

c. 4

d. 5

14. In what year did Metallica win the Catalogue Album of the Year and Catalogue Artist of the Year at the Billboard Music Awards?

    a. 1995

    b. 1997

    c. 1999

    d. 2000

15. What song earned Metallica their first "Best Heavy Metal/Hard Rock Video" at the MTV Video Music Awards?

    a. "Enter Sandman"

    b. "One"

    c. "Until It Sleeps"

    d. "I Disappear"

16. True or False: In 2003, Metallica was nominated for an A.M.A. for "Favorite Alternative Artist."

17. In 2004, Metallica won a PRISM Award for Best Music Video for what song?

    a. "St. Anger"

    b. "Shoot Me Again"

    c. "Frantic"

    d. "Purify"

18. In 2018, Metallica was awarded what award founded by producer Stig Anderson "For international recognition of excellence in the world of music"?

    a. Sibelius Prize
    b. YouTube Music Awards
    c. Winter Conference Awards
    d. Polar Music Prize

19. True or False: Metallica has been nominated for three Juno Awards.

ANSWERS

1. B - 2009

2. D - Jethro Tull

3. A - "One"

4. A - "Stone Cold Crazy"

5. False - *Metallica* was first.

6. C - "Better Than You"

7. B - Best Hard Rock Performance

8. D - 2000

9. False - The album was nominated but did not win.

10. B – "St. Anger"

11. B - 2008

12. False - It was nominated but did not win.

13. A - 2

14. C - 1999

15. A - "Enter Sandman"

16. True

17. C - "Frantic"

18. D - Polar Music Prize

19. True

DID YOU KNOW?

- As of early 2021, Metallica has been nominated for eighteen Grammys and taken home eight. Metallica has also won five Billboard Music Awards.

- Metallica has won two MTV Video Music Awards: the first, in 1992, for "Enter Sandman," and the second, in 1996, for "Until It Sleeps."

- Metallica has also won several international awards, including the Swedish Metal Award in 2009 for "Death Magnetic," Best MTV Video Music Awards in Japan for Best Metal Video for "Hardwired" in 2017, two Metal Hammer Awards, 'Germany' in 2009 for Best Album for *Death Magnetic*, 2013 Best Live Band and 2017 Best International Band, Bandit Rock Awards in Sweden for Best International Group in 2018, Echo Music Prize in 2017 for International Band Award, Top-Selling Album Of the Year in 2009 for *Death Magnetic* from Emma Awards, and three Hungarian Music Awards

- Metallica has won two iHeartRadio Music Awards, the first, in 2017, for Best Album of the Year for *Hardwired… to Self-Destruct*, and the second, for Rock Artist of the Year in 2018.

- Additional awards include: Heavy Music Awards in 2018 award for Best International Band, Heavy Music Awards in 2018 for Best International Band,

2004 ASCAP Pop Music Award for Creative Voice, and the ESPN Action Sports and Music Awards in 2001 for Artist Contribution.

- Metallica and their music have ranked on several of *The Rolling Stone Magazine*'s top lists. Metallica ranks at number sixty-one on the 100 Greatest Artists of All Time. The albums *Master of Puppets* ranks at number two, *Ride the Lightning* at number eleven, *...And Justice for All* at number twenty-one, *Metallica* at number twenty-five, and *Kill 'Em All* at number thirty-five on the 100 Greatest Metal Albums list.

- Numerous awards and nominations from magazines and organizations such as *Billboard Music Awards*, California Music Awards, Classic Rock Awards, Denmark *GAFFA* Awards, and Kerrang! Awards recognize Metallica in various categories.

- Metallica was inducted into the San Francisco Walk of Fame on March 7, 1999, and the mayor of San Francisco at the time, Willie Brown, proclaimed the day "Metallica Day."

- Lars Ulrich was knighted in his home country of Denmark in 2017 for his contributions to music.

CHAPTER 11:

STATS AND RECORDS

TRIVIA TIME!

1. At the time of recording *St. Anger*, Metallica was reported to have approximately how many guitars in their collection?

    a. 200
    b. 350
    c. 500
    d. 800

2. True or False: Metallica is the first band to have a number one mainstream rock song in four different decades.

3. The band not only has performed live events every year since their formation, with the exception of 2001, but they have broken a number of other records as well. How many shows total have Metallica done over the years?

    a. More than 500
    b. More than 900
    c. More than 1600
    d. More than 2000

4. Metallica's self-titled album, or *The Black Album*, as it's more commonly known, spent how many weeks on Billboard's Top 200 Chart?

    a. Close to 200 weeks
    b. Close to 600 weeks
    c. Close to 1000 weeks
    d. Close to 1500 weeks

5. True or False: In 2020, Metallica broke many attendance records in Kentucky, Kansas, and Indiana.

6. Which album of Metallica's sold thousands per week until recently and has sold almost 20 million copies to date?

    a. *Kill 'em All*
    b. *Master of Puppets*
    c. *...And Justice For All*
    d. *The Black Album*

7. True or False: In early October 2019, Metallica released their concert film *S&M2*, which broke a record for the largest ever global rock event cinema release in history, earning over 5.5 million dollars at the box office.

8. Metallica tallied how many streams on Spotify in 2020?

    a. 1.1 million
    b. 99 million
    c. 800 million
    d. 1.1 billion

9. In what year's Guinness World Record book was Metallica recognized for being the first and only band to ever play on all seven continents within one year?

    a. 2010
    b. 2015
    c. 2017
    d. 2019

10. True or False: Metallica has performed in thirty countries.

11. While on their Worldwired Tour in July of 2019, Metallica drew nearly one percent of what country's population, making the event a record-breaking concert?

    a. Finland
    b. Germany
    c. Denmark
    d. Britain

12. Including covers, approximately how many songs have Metallica released in their original, full song form, not including alternate versions of songs?

    a. 120
    b. 170
    c. 230
    d. 280

13. According to concertarchives.org, Metallica has performed at over how many concerts total?

a. 1,000
b. 2,000
c. 3,000
d. 4,000

14. What magazine featured Metallica on their 'World's Highest Paid Celebrities" list in 2019?

    a. *Business Insider*
    b. *People*
    c. *Forbes*
    d. *Entertainment Weekly*

15. How many number one singles has Metallica had on the Billboard Mainstream Rock Songs chart?

    a. Three
    b. Five
    c. Seven
    d. Ten

16. With a play count of around 1680, Metallica's most performed song is which of the following?

    a. "Master of Puppets"
    b. "Enter Sandman"
    c. "Seek and Destroy"
    d. "For Whom the Bell Tolls"

ANSWERS

1. C - 500

2. True

3. C - More than 1600

4. B - Close to 600 weeks

5. False - This occurred in 2019, not 2020.

6. D - *The Black Album*

7. True

8. D - 1.1 billion

9. B - 2015

10. False - Metallica has performed in 60 countries.

11. A - Finland

12. B - 170

13. D - 4,000

14. C - *Forbes*

15. D - Ten

16. A - "Master of Puppets"

DID YOU KNOW?

- As of early 2021, Metallica has released: ten studio albums, eight live albums, three E.P.s, forty-three singles, ten video albums, forty-two music videos, one soundtrack album, one collaboration album, and three box sets.

- In 2019, *Pollstar* claimed Metallica as the biggest touring act in the world, citing their gross ticket sales of $1.4 billion with 22.1 million tickets since 1982.

- As one of the most successful bands in the world, Metallica has sold over 125 million albums worldwide. *The Black Album* is the 12th best-selling album in the U.S. with over 16 million records sold.

- MTV ranked Metallica the third Greatest Heavy Metal Band in History.

- In February 2021, Metallica placed five albums in the Top 10 of Billboard's Top Album Sales Chart and occupied the entire Top 5 of the Vinyl Albums Chart. Walmart's sale of exclusive limited-edition colored vinyl of Metallica's first five L.P.'s (*Kill 'Em All, Ride the Lightning, Master of Puppets, …And Justice For All,* and *Metallica*) and their tenth studio album, *Hardwired… To Self-Destruct,* sparked the achievement.

CHAPTER 12:

ODDS AND ENDS

TRIVIA TIME!

1. For what Disney animated show did Lars Ulrich and James Hetfield voice two dragons?

    a. *American Dragon: Jake Long*
    b. *Dave the Barbarian*
    c. *Dragon Tales*
    d. *Ultimate Book of Spells*

2. Which Metallica member enjoys horror memorabilia and collectibles?

    a. Lars Ulrich
    b. Kirk Hammett
    c. James Hetfield
    d. Jason Newsted

3. Whiskey distiller Mark Pickerell, who helped popularize Maker's Mark, was commissioned in 2017 to craft a whiskey for Metallica. What did they name it?

    a. Fuel
    b. One Whiskey
    c. Whiskey in the Jar

d. Blackened

4. True or False: Metallica performed the Super Bowl half-time show in 2003.

5. A French release of the album *Ride the Lightning* featured a misprinted cover in what color rather than the intended blue?

　　a. Red
　　b. Pink
　　c. Green
　　d. Black

6. In 2013, what guitar company released a Cliff Burton signature bass as a tribute to the late bassist?

　　a. Aria
　　b. Gibson
　　c. Rickenbacker
　　d. Schecter

7. Due to their party-hard lifestyle, Metallica earned what nickname from some media sources?

　　a. Drugtallica
　　b. Glastallica
　　c. Pantallica
　　d. Alcoholica

8. True or False: Lars Ulrich does not have any tattoos.

9. In 1992, while making *The Black Album,* Metallica invited a young fan with the Make-A-Wish Foundation to the studio. Who was this fan that

would also appear in the documentary being filmed at the time?

a. Jake Scott
b. John Smith
c. James Sullivan
d. Jared Shaw

10. What is the name of the album on which Metallica and Lou Reed collaborated?

a. Lou Meets Metal
b. MetalliReed
c. Lulu
d. Lou Underground

11. Since 1983, Metallica has started their live performances with which Ennio Morricone composition?

a. "Ecstasy of Gold"
b. "Lost Boys Calling"
c. "The Wild Bunch"
d. "Here's To You"

12. True or False: Cliff Burton always wore bell-bottoms on stage.

13. Between 1985-1990, members of Metallica played in a secondary band named what, in which they would drink, switch up their roles, and play for fun?

a. Naked Potato
b. Spastik Children
c. Grim Skunk

d. We the Peephole

14. The Metallica logo is its own font called which of the following?

    a. Metal Mania
    b. Pure Evil
    c. 'tallica
    d. Pastor of Puppets

15. Who of Metallica famously appeared on stage typically wearing denim and a Misfits t-shirt?

    a. Cliff Burton
    b. James Hetfield
    c. Kirk Hammett
    d. David Mustaine

16. True or False: At live shows, Kirk Hammett performs a crouching stage move that has been nicknamed the "crab walk."

17. In the song "Enter Sandman," whose child is reciting a bedtime prayer?

    a. James Hetfield
    b. Bob Rock
    c. Lars Ulrich
    d. Kirk Hammet

18. What item previously belonging to Cliff Burton does James Hetfield often wear?

    a. Gold cross necklace
    b. Leather wrist band

c. Silver skull ring

d. Hematite snake ring

19. According to the Encyclopedia Metallica, which of these names were not shortlisted by Lars Ulrich and James Hetfield for the band prior to settling on Metallica?

    a. Blitzer
    b. Hellbound
    c. Grinder
    d. Red Vette

20. True or False: James Hetfield tapes his hand to protect it from getting cut up from his rapid, intense guitar playing.

ANSWERS

1. B - Dave the Barbarian

2. B - Kirk Hammett

3. D - Blackened

4. False - Metallica has never performed at the Super Bowl.

5. C - Green

6. A - Aria

7. D - Alcohollica

8. True

9. B - John Smith

10. C - Lulu

11. A - "Ecstasy of Gold"

12. True

13. B - Spastik Children

14. D - Pastor of Puppets

15. A - Cliff Burton

16. False - Robert Trujillo does the "crab walk."

17. B - Bob Rock's son

18. C - Silver skull ring

19. B - Hellbound

20. False - Kirk Hammet tapes his hand

DID YOU KNOW?

- James Hetfield broke his arm or wrist enough times while skateboarding that his management company, Q Prime, wrote a clause in his contract forbidding him from skateboarding while Metallica was touring.

- Cliff Burton started playing bass at the age of thirteen after the death of his brother, Scott. According to his parents, Cliff would say, "I am going to be the best bassist for my brother" and would practice up to six hours per day.

- When the members of Metallica were personally divided, they rented military barracks to set up a make-shift studio. These were where the album *St. Anger* was partially recorded. The intention was to make the band "uncomfortable" and also to foster a garage band feel on the album.

- There is a spoof band that combines the music of Metallica and The Beatles, called Beatallica. The band was nearly shut down by the owners of the rights to The Beatles' music, Sony/ATV Music Publishing. A cease and desist notice was issued; however, Lars Ulrich asked Metallica's attorney to help Beatallica sort things out with Sony. A few mentionable Beatallica releases include "Sgt.

Hetfield's Motorbreath Pub Band" and "Blackened in The U.S.S.R."

- Metallica has a few nicknames to refer to adventurous young women who were willing to hang out with the band after shows. "Ednas" was a general term, and "Tub Tarts" referred to those who would get in the shower.

- John Bush, the singer of Anthrax, turned down an opportunity to be the singer for Metallica. Following the release of Metallica's debut album, James Hetfield wanted to focus solely on guitar and personally invited John to be the lead singer, but he declined.

- When recording the album *Master of Puppets*, Ulrich was striving for a specific snare drum sound from a Ludwig Black Beauty snare. Rick Allen from Def Leppard had one but was recovering from the loss of his left arm. Ulrich reached out to their manager and was able to have the snare overnighted to Denmark.

CHAPTER 13:

METALLICA TODAY

TRIVIA TIME!

1. What is the name of Metallica's workforce initiative that provides support to community colleges in order to enhance their career and technical education programs and provide funding for students?
   a. The Metallica Scholars
   b. School of Metallica
   c. The Metallica Initiative
   d. Metallica Cares

2. Starting during the pandemic of 2020, Metallica streamed free shows from their archives for a weekly concert series called what?
   a. Metallica Mania
   b. Metallica Mondays
   c. Weekly Metallica
   d. Whammy Wednesdays

3. After playing on all seven continents, where did Kirk Hammett mention wanting to play next?
   a. The Moon
   b. The Pacific Ocean

c. Mars

d. The International Space Station

4. True or False: In 2018, Metallica unveiled a new line of Rolex watches with designs representing the artwork from their albums.

5. Lars Ulrich said he was "hellbent" that the band play at which major festival someday?

    a. Electric Daisy Carnival
    b. Donauinselfest
    c. Coachella
    d. Mawazine

6. Who did Metallica partner up with for a planned festival tour in 2020 before having to cancel due to COVID-19?

    a. C3 Presents
    b. Danny Wimmer Presents
    c. A.E.G. Presents
    d. Jimmy McGill Presents

7. Which member of Metallica has a passion for art, collecting and selling pieces to and from his collection?

    a. Robert Trujillo
    b. Kirk Hammett
    c. Lars Ulrich
    d. James Hetfield

8. True or False: One of the band's most recent albums, *S&M2*, charted at #5 in the Billboard Top 200.

9. Which Metallica member is a mechanic in his spare time and also enjoys classic cars?

    a. Robert Trujillo
    b. James Hetfield
    c. Lars Ulrich
    d. Kirk Hammett

10. Metallica is scoring music for a 2021 Disney movie release. What is the title of the movie, starring Dwayne Johnson and Emily Blunt?

    a. *Jungle Cruise*
    b. *Rock Bottom*
    c. *Raya and the Last Dragon*
    d. *Frozen 3*

11. Horror comics, posters, figurines, and memorabilia are all a part of the collection of which Metallica member?

    a. James Hetfield
    b. Kirk Hammett
    c. Lars Ulrich
    d. Robert Trujillo

12. True or False: In promotion of their 2020 drive-in concert, Metallica sold Pandemica! merchandise and t-shirts.

13. In 2017, Metallica announced the formation of their charity dedicated to supporting workforce education, feeding the hungry, and other services to

aid in creating sustainable communities. What is this charity named?

   a. Hero of the Day
   b. Turn the Page
   c. Wherever I May Roam
   d. All Within My Hands

14. In September of 2019, Metallica played two shows with the San Francisco Symphony at what newly opened venue?

   a. The Fillmore
   b. The Warfield
   c. The Chase Center
   d. Davies Symphony Hall

15. Which member of Metallica is quoted saying that the "band's best album is yet to come"?

   a. James Hetfield
   b. Kirk Hammett
   c. Lars Ulrich
   d. Robert Trujillo

16. True or False: Former Metallica member Jason Newsted owns a music publishing company called Jasonic.

17. What song did Metallica perform a virtual acoustic version of, tagging 2020 onto the name of the original title?

   a. "Fade to Black 2020"

b. "Blackened 2020"

c. "Escape 2020"

d. "Through the Never 2020"

18. What band was scheduled to tour South America with Metallica in 2020, which has been postponed due to the coronavirus pandemic?

a. Guns 'n Roses

b. Elton John

c. Slipknot

d. Greta van Fleet

19. In addition to their other charity work, Metallica was involved in the construction of what country's first children's cancer hospital?

a. Romania

b. Bulgaria

c. Turkey

d. Serbia

20. Along with other rock and metal bands such as Slipknot, Rage Against the Machine, and Guns N' Roses, Metallica will be featured in a March 2021 documentary release titled what?

a. *Long Live Rock*

b. *Ready to Rock*

c. *Rock of Ages*

d. *Rock Forever*

ANSWERS

1. A - The Metallica Scholars
2. B - Metallica Mondays
3. D - The International Space Station
4. False - Nixon watches
5. C - Coachella
6. B - Danny Wimmer Presents
7. C - Lars Ulrich
8. False - *S&M2* charted at number 4.
9. B - James Hetfield
10. A - *Jungle Cruise*
11. B - Kirk Hammett
12. True
13. D - All Within My Hands
14. C - The Chase Center
15. C - Lars Ulrich
16. True
17. B - "Blackened 2020"
18. D - Greta van Fleet
19. A - Romania
20. A - *Long Live Rock*

DID YOU KNOW?

- James Hetfield married Francesca Hetfield in 1997, and they have three children. Lars Ulrich married model Jessica Miller in 2015. He was married twice before and has three children between his previous wives. Kirk Hammett married twice and has remained married to his second wife, Lani, since 1998. They have two sons. Robert Trujillo is married to Chloe Trujillo, and they have two children.

- Cliff Burton's father, Ray Burton, used the royalties earned from Metallica's first three albums to fund music scholarships for students at Castro Valley High School, where Cliff went to high school.

- On August 16, 2019, Metallica performed for BlizzCon, an annual gaming convention held by Blizzard Entertainment. Being a virtual event, the video game live-streaming service Twitch was one of the places to watch it. Due to some unfortunate mistakes dealing with proper licensure for the music, Metallica's performance was dubbed over on the Twitch livestream with royalty-free music.

- James Hetfield creates artwork for Metallica merchandise, such as the "Papa Het Pick Tin" that includes a tin with picks featuring designs by him and Dirty Donny. During the COVID-19 pandemic, he made handmade end tables that include a signature of "Papa H."

- In 2020, the All Within My Hands (A.W.M.H.) organization donated to wildfire relief efforts, Feeding America, the American Association of Community Colleges, and COVID-19 disaster relief efforts.

- In 2020, Metallica live-streamed a pre-Super Bowl concert the night before Super Bowl LIV called "The Night Before," a sold-out show at San Francisco's AT&T Park that was free to view online.

- On February 7th of 2021, Metallica performed on *A Late Show with Stephen Colbert: Super Bowl Edition*. The following month, on March 3rd they returned for a second show, just because.

- Following the winter snow storm that severely affected the southern U.S., especially Texas, in 2021, through the All Within My Hands Foundation, Metallica donated money to Texas food banks and toward helping victims of the storm.

- Metallica is scheduled to headline two nights at the Aftershock Festival in October 2021 at Discovery Park in Sacramento, California.

- In recent interviews, the band has confirmed that they are working on new music for an album release in the near future, possibly in 2021.

WRAPPING UP

Now that you have finished reading *The Badass Metallica Trivia Book*, you are a knowledgeable fan of one of the greatest metal bands in the world. As their legacy continues to unfold, we anticipate Metallica's future endeavors and music to come.

Please review the book where you bought it and we hope to see your positive feedback.

CPSIA information can be obtained
at www.ICGtesting.com
Printed in the USA
BVHW052352210423
662811BV00013B/1285

9 781955 149022